Regina's

By Margaret Clyne
Illustrated by Linda Hendry

Houghton Mifflin Company • Boston
Atlanta • Dallas • Geneva, Illinois • Palo Alto • Princeton

Regina had lost her glasses. When she got new ones, her mom said, "When they're not on your face, put them in their case."

When Regina watched television, she put on her glasses. Afterwards she said, "When they're not on your face, put them in their case."

When Regina was drawing, she put on her glasses. Afterwards she said, "When they're not on your face, put them in their case."

When she was reading, she put on her glasses. Afterwards she said, “When they’re not on your face, put them in their case.”

Then one day Regina came in from playing. She couldn't find her glasses. She looked under the television. Her mom looked on her desk. Her dad looked behind the bookcase. Everybody hunted for her glasses. Then Regina looked outside.

Regina smiled and said, “We need another rhyme: when they’re in the case, find a very safe place!”